Silent Voices from Forever

DAVID BROWN

Published by JNB Publishing Limited
The Treacle Factory,
2a Reginald Street,
Luton, Bedfordshire
LU2 7QZ

A catalogue record for this book
is available from the British Library

ISBN 978-0-9555239-1-5

This book is dedicated to Jane ~

in this life my lover, wife, best friend, partner;
now my soulmate; my Beloved.

Forever, forever and forever.

Jane Brown
1950 – 2006
Never Gone, Never Far...

Contents

Preface – A Gift of Love to You   i

Acknowledgments   ii

Introduction   1

From My Beloved   7

Love Is The Only Reality   9

God Is...   11

I Am   13

You Are   15

Where All Is Peace   17

Spirit Is...   19

All Beauty   21

The Light Will Never Fail Us   23

There Is But Light   25

Christ Is...   26

Formless Beauty   29

Touching Heaven   31

Spirit   33

Energy Is...   34

Always Together   37

Painting Your Sunrise   39

Home At Last   40

Dying Is...   43

Every Now and Then   45

Happy Birthday, Jane   47

All Is Well   49

Eternal Life Is...   51

I Saw You Today My Beloved   53

Let's Go Deeper, My Love   55

Nothing Ends   57

Vibration Is...   59

The Glimpse Behind The Veil   61

Divine Mother   63

The Light That Shines From Heaven   64

Justice Is...   67

You Can See Me   68

Beyond God   71

The World Of Spirit   73

The World Is...   75

Never Be The Same Again   77

The True Reality   79

True Peace And Joy   81

Heaven Is...   83

Death Is...   85

Afterword   87

A Gift of Love to You

Your loved ones who have slipped from your sight are not dead. They really do live on in another dimension; vibrating at a frequency too fine for your physical eyes to see or ears to hear. They are not far from you and are only a thought away.

You (or someone you know) may be grieving for a wife, husband, lover; you may have lost a child. You may be suffering from the feelings of loss at the passing of your mother, father, sister, brother or dearest friend. Your loved ones are not lost to you, or you to them – and one day you will see them again. They do not suffer now; they are free from the encumbrances and limitations of the physical body. They do not weep and are not sorrowful, yet they are sometimes constrained in their joy when feeling your sorrow. They love you still – and that love can never die.

You may sense their presence at any time, sometimes in nature's unquestionable signs, in the synchronicity of events or an inexplicable awareness of a familiar aroma or piece of music. You may hear their voice calling you in the night. They may visit you in a dream or appear to you visibly in spirit form while you are awake. You may find yourself radiantly happy for no apparent reason as they smile within your heart. They may brush your skin or hug you when you are lonely. You can connect with them through your own deep contemplation and silence.

They will be there for you, waiting, when it is time to make your transition to the blessed subtle realms of God.

This book is their gift to you. They gave the words to me so that I could give them to you. My prayer is that you will find comfort and healing from these love letters sent from the Beloved.

Take courage – do not be afraid; there is no death. Love can never die.

David Brown

With my grateful thanks to...

wonderful men and women of God who, knowingly or unknowingly, have helped me to find my way – on to this my most recent stage of the great, unending journey of Life... especially Miranda, Martin and Peter, Founder and faculty tutors of the Interfaith Seminary, London... Lindsay, for so lovingly opening a door that had been locked to me by my past spiritual conditioning...John Tunbridge, spiritual guide, for his reassurance and encouragement...Sarah Tyler-Walters, spiritual teacher and mentor...the writers, ancient and modern, who have enshrined spiritual wisdom and direction in the pages of books, sacred texts and scriptures... especially the teachings of the great guru Paramahansa Yogananda, Founder of Self Realisation Fellowship worldwide...

the amazing photographers who have captured so beautifully the glory of creation... for photos.com...

Jeremy and Ian of JNB Publishing Ltd, publishers of this book...

my precious and extraordinary family, Jeremy, Louise and Joanna for their constant support and encouragement. It was Louise who first suggested that these messages could help people if collated into book form, which has now become this book. It was Louise who lovingly and meticulously selected every individual photograph to complement every message. It was Louise who was honest in her criticism and full of encouragement when we worked together on compiling the manuscript. I personally think this book should be credited to David Brown with Louise Williams but she has refused to accept the credit for what is rightly hers...

the silent voices from Forever, without whom there would have been no book...

Jane, my soulmate; one of those silent voices...

Introduction

As Jane's breathing began to change, the nurse turned to me as my eldest daughter and I sat by my wife's bedside and said: "Is there someone you should call?" Suddenly it occurred to us that Jane was actually in the process of dying. We had become so accustomed to loving her, caring for her and believing that somehow – something – would happen to miraculously heal her that it was a shock when the realisation dawned upon us that she was close to death. Joanna, my daughter, and I looked at each other and she immediately got up and ran out of the room to call my son and my youngest daughter to get to the hospice as soon as possible – if not sooner! They were already on their way when they got Joanna's call. Back in the hospice room, Jane's breathing had become increasingly laboured. The nurse, Joanna and I were just sitting there, feeling helpless, holding Jane's hand and just staring longingly at her. Suddenly, a voice within me seemed to say: "Help her... remind her of who she is..." I responded within my mind: "What the heck are we all doing here, staring at a dying body when this beautiful Soul is needing our love and help to make her transition?" I hurried to reach instinctively for the book that she and I had been reading daily during her sickness; it was 'A Course In Miracles' (Foundation for Inner Peace 1975) which is a modern text written in the first person as from Jesus, dictated inwardly to the author Helen Schucman. I said loudly, "Jane, I know you can hear me; if you're able, – say these words after me: I am not weak, but strong... I am not helpless, but all-powerful... I am not limited, but unlimited... I am not doubtful, but certain..." (Lesson 91 ACIM). As soon as I began to say these sentences, Jane stopped breathing in the laborious way that she had been for the past hour, breathed one last deep breath and was free. Joanna looked at me, stunned. The nurse had expected Jane to continue to labour for some time and had left the room. Jane had other ideas, and on the frequency that words of Truth vibrate, her Real Self was able to leave the physical body. At the precise moment that she breathed for the last time, the door flung open and our son, Jeremy, and Louise, our youngest daughter, burst into the room. From her standpoint in her subtle body, Jane could obviously see them arriving, desperate to park the car; running up the stairs of the hospice, racing down the corridor towards her room and then, content that they were with her physical body at the precise moment of her passing, to watch us all hug and kiss her now lifeless body.

From the very second that Jane passed, my life changed in every detail. I made the decision to open myself to the reality and to the pain, rather than to hide from the feelings of grief and loss that came like waves at any time of the day or night. With help from some really 'special' people, especially Miranda, the Founder of the Interfaith Seminary, I learned to stay open and to soften when the worst waves crashed in to devastating effect. In this way, softening and opening, I found a way to transform seemingly overwhelming painful emotions into positive energy. During the months that followed Jane's passing, so many extraordinary and astonishing things happened that I no longer simply believed in life after death – I actually knew it to be a greater reality than the life we live in the body here on earth. 'Jane's' spirit, and therefore other loved ones who have passed, have survived death and are able to communicate and continue to connect with me; so long as the love connection on my part remains strong enough and the method of meditation is sufficiently spiritually scientific and authentic. I literally plunged into the Limitless Presence of God, suspending all former belief structures and ideas in search of answers and reality. I was a baby in a vast universe and, like all babies, able to learn a new language and open to new experiences on an intuitive level.

I practise meditation on God regularly; merging, or dissolving, the self with higher levels of consciousness and, ultimately, with the Spirit. During a particular period of silent meditation alone, I felt my left arm begin to move involuntarily. It lifted from its position resting on my thigh, took a backwards circular arc so that the palm of my hand was facing the ground and my elbow was in the air behind my back, then with a firm and certain motion completed a full 360 degree circumference much like the bowling action of a cricketer, before my hand landed with a thud on the table by the side of my meditation chair. I slightly opened my eyes to 'peek' a look at where my hand had landed. Sitting directly under my hand was a pen. It was there because I would often use it to write my meditation journal. Never before, however, has anything remotely like this happened to me. The movement of my arm was initiated by intelligence other than my own. As if in an act of obedience, I took the pen in my left hand and simply placed it on a blank page of my open journal. After three or four seconds, my hand was moving in a disciplined manner across the page; I was not in charge of this occurrence and I was not the initiator. After about fifteen minutes of constant guided motion of the pen in my hand, the energy that was moving my hand withdrew and all inclination to move it further ceased. I slowly came out of my meditative state and looked at the page in my journal. I was absolutely stunned at what I saw. My hand had been guided to draw symbols and hieroglyphics that I could never have drawn in a million years.

Over the next few weeks, the experience occurred with some regularity. I was afraid to tell anyone what was happening, or to show anyone the drawings and symbols. I decided to deliberately separate my daily meditation practice into two distinct periods at different times during the day; the main period I made a conscious decision to stay fixed on God and I stated in my opening time of prayer that this session was for God alone and that I would resist any movements in my arm or any communications from 'beyond'. The second period of meditation I also gave to God but asked for grace to respond if the intelligence, or energies, that were using this method of connection were permitted to do so by God. During one such session, the 'spirit drawing' became 'spirit writing'. Slowly and deliberately, the pen began to spell out words as distinct from symbols. I began to recognise patterns and the regular use of particular symbols to express certain thoughts. I slowly dared to submit questions and was amazed to receive profound and yet very direct and straightforward answers. Buoyed by this level of boldness in my understanding of what was happening, I found myself asking stupid, self-obsessed questions and there was a complete immobility of the pen in my hand in silent reply. I was left in no doubt whatsoever that this was a means of connection and communication between the earth realm and the spirit world. I took my courage in my hands and decided to share with my family what had been happening to me.

I was extremely nervous as I invited my two daughters, each individually on separate occasions, to come to my meditation room so that I could show them the 'spirit drawings' and 'writings'. To say that I was nervous is an understatement; in fact, I was scared stiff at what they might say. I expected them to think that I was going crazy; that I was concocting the whole thing as a form of self-therapy or delusive condition. I was surprised at their response. As I turned each page, their face showed an expression of amazement and appreciation of what they saw. Encouraged, but still unsure of what was behind the phenomena that I was experiencing, I decided to seek out spiritual men and women who could validate the 'spirit writing', or alternatively, guide me in a more sensible and appropriate direction. It was almost impossible to find anyone in conventional religious circles who could even open their minds to the possibility of there being any reality to survival of physical death and the potential for continuing communication with those in the subtle realms, other than as being either something limited to a theory that has no practical relevance, elevated to a mystery that cannot even begin to be explored or simply dismissed as a 'work of the devil'.

I read a great amount: books written by spiritual masters and teachers from all the spiritual paths and also books written by philosophers, metaphysicians and quantum physicists. I consulted respected teachers from a variety of spiritual perspectives and am grateful for these 'mighty companions', especially those from the Interfaith Seminary, the Spiritualist Association of Great Britain, the College of Psychic Studies and the Self Realisation Fellowship in London. I realised that the earliest of mediums for communication between the Spirit and humans on earth was through 'automatic writing'. Authors of all the world's sacred texts have pointed to the actual authorship of scripture coming not from their own mind, but from Spirit. In the early days of scientific Spiritism (before 'platform mediums' and the like), automatic writing was the only medium for such communication, producing libraries full of outstanding philosophical answers to some of life's greatest mysteries and also proving through indisputable evidence, the survival of the individual soul after physical death. I went on to learn that there is also a distinction between 'inspirational writing', which is when the initiative for what is written comes from the writer under the inspiration of Spirit, and 'automatic writing', when the initiative originates and emanates from Spirit and the writer is the servant of Spirit.

The collection of writings that make up this little book are a mixture: some inspirational and some automatic writings. I spent a number of months in regular daily meditation on the sunrise and also on the sunset; a practice I would recommend to anyone, especially those recently bereaved; most of the inspirational writings came as a result of those meditations. Other writings were the product of automatic writing, initiated by Spirit, usually towards the end of one of my routine morning or evening meditations. In such cases the message came, not from my mind, or me, but from eternity; the realm of bliss I like to call 'Forever'.

I do not consider this book to be a collection of poems, but rather, messages from those who have passed out of this physical body but who do not stop loving those who are left behind. If you are reading this book, somewhere within its covers may be a message of hope and healing for you.

From My Beloved

Be not afraid; there is no death.
I saw my body fall,
I heard your tears.
I was at my body's funeral,
I felt your love.
I have seen you weep, but
I am not dead.

You have felt my touch in the night
Like the brush of an angel's wing.
You have caught a glimpse of my presence
As I have visited you in your sorrow.
You have heard me singing to you
In the music of your mind.
We still are One;
Love can never die.
It is stronger than a thousand waves
Upon the ocean;
Stronger than the ocean itself.

If you are still –
When you can reach inside your heart –
You can, and will, find me.
Yes, you can truly reach and find me.
For how can we who are One
Ever be separate?
How can we who are One
Ever be divided?
Now our special relationship
Has become a holy relationship.
I am not dead;
I did not die.
All is well.

Love Is The Only Reality

There is but one thing of which you can be certain.
Love can never die,
Because Love is the only Reality.
All other states and appearances
Are merely experiences;
Those which are gained on your journey Home;
Home to Love.

It is here that you will know Reality
No more passing from life to apparent death.
It is here in Heaven that you will be fully awake.
All other loves are like the flame of a match
Compared to the sun.
All other beauty like the reflection in a mirror
Compared to its source.

Accept each day;
Each hour;
Each moment
As an opportunity to take the next
Careful step Home
Where you will meet your Real Self
And those whom you have loved
And thought lost.

And there will be no more parting of the ways
For there you will know that Reality
Has been found at last.
Perfect Oneness.
Perfect Unity.
Perfect Love.

God Is...

God is not able to be explained nor understood.
God is 'Not this... Not that'.
God is 'I Am'.

God is Mother – Father – Originator
From which all else is a reflection.

God is the source of consciousness,
Cosmic consciousness.
The super Intelligence;
Ultimate Awareness.
Oneness; perfect unity
From which individuality returns.

Intelligence defines Which-ness
As Whom-ness;
Though genderless to Whom
Genders return.
God is formless,
To Whom forms return.

God is the source of energy
Without being energy.

God is perfection;
The state to which all shades
And expressions of good and evil return.

God is Not this... Not that,
But Is.
God Is...

I Am

I am formless and I am.
I am not this, or that;
I am Spirit.

I do not look at myself in a mirror;
I have no need to see my beauty.
I am Beauty.

I can be on the Earth;
I can be on other worlds.
I can be in Heaven;
I am Being.

I can be seen in form or
I can be formless.
I can be who I was on earth;
I can be who I am in Heaven.
I can see my loved ones –
I can feel their love;
I am Love.

I laugh;
I am Laughter.
I sing;
I am Music.
I smile;
I am Happiness.
I Am.

You Are

Loved.
Loved without conditions;
Loved totally;
Completely, unreservedly.
You are connected
To the very Source of Love
By who you are.

You are never separated,
Isolated or alone.
We are connected.
Now and always.
Forever we remain connected.

You are Love
Itself.
A healing power,
You are.

You are spirit;
God's Spirit living as a soul
Clothed in a body
To grace the earth.
To love humanity;
To heal the lonely;
To reconnect broken hearts
Who have forgotten who they are.
Beautiful, all powerful,
Limitless Spirit
Living as souls, just as...
You are.

Where All Is Peace

My gift to you
Is peace; deep peace.
I have been given such peace,
In such amazing abundance.
I have plunged into its beautiful depths,
I have tasted it,
Felt it;
I have bathed in it,
Splashed around like a small child
Laughing and playing with its colours,
Beautiful, calm, peaceful colours.
Lovely golden layer and hue,
Melding into another;
Playing songs of worship
To the Prince of Peace;
The Author of Peace;
The Creator of Peace.

I have forgotten the cares of care,
The storms of worry and strife.
No longer can fear come even near me,
For it exists not in Reality,
Where all is peace.
Such peace, that it passes understanding.
It cannot be described
In words to satisfy your intellect.
But it can be felt.
You too can plunge into its beautiful ocean.
And that is my gift to you today,
My love.
My beloved.
That you take my hand,
And come where I am.
In Peace.

Spirit Is...

God is Spirit and Spirit is God;
One and the same.
God is Father, Spirit is Mother – perfect unity;
Genderless and with no shade of change.

One Spirit; One God.
Both passive and active,
Formless, bringing form into being.
Perfect being allowing becoming
To be a possibility.
Spirit is emanation;
The Emanation of all wisdom, all knowledge.
The Emanation of all possibility
Of what has been, could be and ever may be.

Spirit is Transcendence;
The Transcendence of all that is limiting;
The means of transcending limitation.
Spirit has no boundaries; is omnipresent;
Spirit is omnipotent,
Within and without; above and below,
Around and about.

Spirit is silence yet speaks.
Spirit is invisible yet reveals.
Spirit is formless yet burns like fire.
Spirit is No-thing yet is All There Is.
Spirit is Love.
Spirit is Peace.
Spirit is Joy.
Spirit is Holy.
Holy Spirit.
Spirit Is...

All Beauty

You see the spirit world with your heart.
It is all beauty and it is all peace.
It is great and wonderful.

It knows no time;
Only cycles.
It knows no space;
Near and far are one.

It has not any voice
Yet communication is perfect.

Only love has it in common with the Earth,
Or the World.

Yet the Earth is its Womb
And the World are its Children.

You were never born; you will never die.
You have never changed; you can never change.
Unborn, eternal, immutable, immemorial,
You do not die when the body dies.

Bhagavad Gita 2:20

The Light Will Never Fail Us

The Light sweeps majestically
Into every day.
It comes despite the darkness
Piercing the clouds.

The light brings healing and hope
Into every heart.
It is certain and sure;
Never wavering or doubting.

It comes despite all odds;
Despite our fear and unbelief
Shaming us into faith once more
That the Light will never fail us.

O Holy Spirit come,
Come into my day and sweep all darkness away.
Dispel the fear and unbelief.

Shame me into faith once more
By your sheer beauty and certainty –
Come.

There Is But Light

It comes again; never failing
The light to prove our way.
Last night it died in blazing beauty;
This morning the resurrection.

This rising today is less glorious
Than its death,
Yet how beautiful and glorious it still is.
Fighting graciously to pierce the earth,
Probing until the forces of darkness yield;
Yielding inevitably, helplessly to the light.

There is no death;
There is but life.
There is no darkness;
There is but light.

And there will be no more night;
They need no light of lamp or sun,
For the Sovereign God will be their light,
And they will reign forever and ever.

Revelation 22:5

25

Christ Is...

The Perfect Creation.
Caused by the Perfect Love of God the Spirit.
Christ is The Consciousness of God.
The only Consciousness.
The Way to Everything that there is.
The Way to Everything that could possibly be.

Christ's Consciousness is The Truth,
To which all forms of truth return.
Christ's Consciousness is Deathless Life.
Never born and never dying,
Forever awake, forever living.
Perfect in rest;
Unlimited creativity.
Compassionately active.

Christ is Krishna.
Christ is Buddha.
Christ is Jesus.

Christ is the maggot and the worm.
Christ is the beauty that is in the rose.
Christ is the majesty in the oak.
Christ is the Universe.
Christ is a billion, billion galaxies.

Christ is the nurse in the hospital ward.
Christ is the one weeping by the dying.
Christ is the one dying.
Christ is the Guide.
Christ is Salvation.
Christ is Heaven.
Christ is Hell.

There is nothing outside Christ.
Christ is the all in All.
No fear; no guilt; no darkness,
No sin; no judgement; no death,
No separation; no isolation.

Christ is Consciousness.
Christ is Love.
Christ is Unconditional.
Christ is Unconditional Conscious Love.
Christ Is...

Formless Beauty

The beauty of the formless
Is greater than that of form.

Have you seen the sunrise
Break slowly, formlessly across the skies
Drawing back a curtain of darkness
Revealing an illuminated stage
Upon which the world can play?

It is formless
Yet it is all Beauty.

Have you seen the sunset
As the glorious light makes it bow?
It has magnificently played a leading role
Upon life's stage and now it moves invisibly
To illuminate another stage in a faraway land;
Invisible to you yet unfolding
In the sight of your brother.

Formless;
Beautiful;
Glory.

Touching Heaven

The beauty of the World of Spirit –
That which you call the Other Side –
Is incomprehensible to your minds.
The beauty awaiting you
When you are free from your earthly bodies
Is too wonderful for your eyes to behold.
With new bodies, equipped for these
Realms of Beauty,
We behold sights and sounds
Which manifest at a frequency too fast and
Too subtle for your earthly senses.

When you gaze without thought
At the sunrise or sunset
You are catching but the merest glimpse
Of Beauty; yet even then it is too
Beautiful for your body's mind to grasp.

Think for a moment how glorious it is
When we, whom you have loved,
Slip free from the heaviness of our
Earthly bodies and soar into worlds
Of wonder and Beauty with eyes
That are equipped to behold these sights.

When you are still – when you reach beyond –
And when you open to Love and Spirit
You can catch a glimpse; hear the sounds of Beauty.

But for now, remember, you cannot see
Us with your body's eyes
But with your heart.
Cannot hear us with your ears
But with your Mind
Cannot feel us with your body
But with your soul.

And in that way, you can bring
Heaven to Earth
And Earth can touch Heaven.

Spirit

If this indescribable beauty be but a dream,
If, when we awake from sleep
We simply dream;
In the sleep called death
We are more truly awake
Than anything we have yet seen or known
In this beautiful dream called life.

From the dream of death
We will awaken again
Seeing sights too wonderful to be known
By our minds still merely
Dreaming of such beauty.

Slowly, we arise from the lovely
Dream called death
Not simply in a body;
Though for some,
For a season
That may be their choice,
But in Spirit;
As Beauty Itself;
Not merely beholding Beauty's lovely Presence
But being It;
Feeling It
Experiencing It;
Extending It to a Universe of universes
To a billion, billion planets;
Penetrating time,
Awakening creation from its dream;
Revealing Reality.

Energy Is...

Energy is the result of Consciousness
Merging with the will of Intelligence,
A Divine Marriage.
A Holy Union.
Consummation of Perfect Love.
Lover and Beloved,
Becoming Mother – Father.
Always One; still One.
The Beginning and End of Love
Producing seed; the seed of Life,
The seed of All life,
Without which nothing can live,
Nor be seen or be touched.
The seed, having been produced
Through the consummation of Perfect Love,
With Perfect Love,
Cannot be destroyed.
It does not sustain Life,
It is Life.

It does not create life in various forms,
For lives are expressions of Life.
The Seed is Life Itself.
It is the Life Source.
It is the very power of Life.
Nothing exists of itself.
Think of an apple; a tree; a flower.
It is made of the Seed.

Think of a baby.
It is made of the Seed.
Think of mankind.
It is made of the Seed.
Think of the Universe.
It is made of the Seed.
Think of a table; a book; a chair.
All is made of the Seed.
Nothing exists of itself.
Energy is the Seed of God.
Energy issues from the Will of God,
The substance of Life itself.
Energy Is...

Always Together

I saw you today, my Love;
In that Holy Instant you saw me.
Our eyes met –
You saw my loving smile –
That long-remembered loving smile.

In that instant,
All was beauty;
All was peace.
At last, you know for sure,
There is no death.
I am here;
And though you seem there
We are in truth, together.
One;
As we have always been One.
There is no separation.
Now, for a time, you feel separate;
All separation shall end
And we shall feel the truth.
In the moments when we seem apart
Turn that moment into an instant;
A Holy Instant.
For in each Holy Instant
Where time stands still,
And is no more,
We will feel each other.

And if you will look through the veil
You will see me
As I see you.
As you saw me
In that Holy Instant
Just Now.

Painting Your Sunrise

It's great fun
Painting beauty in the heavens;
Spreading my canvas
For all to see;
Eating the fruit of my own creation;
Sharing times of joy and laughter
With all.

But my greatest pleasure
Is when I help you
Show Love and mercy
Upon the earth.
For here we have all we need.
What is needed more
Is peace on Earth.

And lo, I am with you always,
To the end of the age.

Matthew 28:20

Home At Last

O God my heart longs to be
Where the music of the universe
Has replaced the noise of traffic roar.

To be in the clouds
Where my eyes behold Love;
Where no more does the darkness
Of hatred hang heavy
Upon the heart.

I long to open my eyes
To see my loved ones;
Those of beauty and joy
Who once graced my life with their love.
To see them smile;
To mould into the presence,
Bursting the unreal bubble of loneliness
Pervading this overcrowded globe.

I long to see colour;
Colours deep speaking
In sounds so subtle
That all knowledge is known.
To gaze on colours that paint
Beauty on the canvass of an earth sunrise,
Dismissing a storm cloud
With one stroke of the artist hand.

I long to see God;
The mind that formed all being
And becoming.
I long to fall at the Feet
Of Creation and know that
I am Home at last.

I long to soar in the Realms of Heaven;
Over fields and mountains
Created by heavenly thought
Devoid of destruction and death
Produced by earthly thoughts.

I long to see Heaven
As a bird sees the Earth;
Free.
Free at last.

Dying is...

Living to God.
It is to awaken;
To rise from the dream,
This dream of life,
Yet which is not real life at all.

For this dream life
Is change,
And never real.
It is full of delusion
And suffering
And appears to end
With death,
While dying is to arise;
To fly into reality
And to know;
To know endless bliss
Inside and outside;
Above and below,
Around and all about;
To be light, and colour,
and sound.
To see clearly and to be seen.
To remember all whom have loved,
And been loved.

Dying is transition.
Dying is growth.
Dying is expansion.
Dying is freedom.
Dying is ecstasy.
Dying is love.
Dying is to live.
Dying is.

Every Now and Then

Every now and then,
When lost in the wonder of it all;
You know for certain –
An awareness arises from deep within,
That what you see with your eyes
Is merely a curtain
Draped across a stage.

There behind that curtain
Is another world;
A world full of love and laughter,
Healing and wholeness.
And see –
Just then –
Every now and then;
You begin to see it for yourself.

Scenes of beauty;
Forms of loved ones;
In those blissful moments,
Every now and then,
It's as though you see God
Saying "All is well";
"Be not afraid".
"You are never alone".

Every now and then,
When the curtain parts
And the Stage is revealed,
You know that the waiting
Is but for a season.
That one sweet day
We shall all play our part together;
In the cast
Of the Song of the Universe.

So for now we watch –
Watch, wait and applaud.
Every now and then.

Happy Birthday, Jane

For fifty-five years you lived on earth.
What a blessing you gave to the world.
You spread love, joy and laughter.

None who met you will ever forget you.
Now, gone from our eyes.
But not from our hearts,
Our love for you is renewed today.

Happy birthday, Jane.

All Is Well

It is good to be free.
To soar, to fly; now that I am free,
Free to be me.

I never thought such beauty could be,
Was ever here; is here.
I now can speak, though not in words
Such as you speak words
To ears; through mouths.
I speak in thoughts
Of love... great love.

I can be; I can become.
I can meld or I can be one.
But most of all, I can love,
Feel love; for all is love.

There is no pain.
There is no death.
All are here; these you call 'They'.
We are all One; able to be,
And to become.

I can help for I am Helper.
I can help you, you whom I love.
I am one with Love,
And one with you.
All is well.

Eternal Life Is...

The Reality of Existence;
Consciousness –
All that is
Knowing, knowledge.

Eternal life is infinite;
Infinity –
Outside of space and time.
There is no death;
No birth –
No beginning nor end.

Eternal life is Heaven and Earth.
It is always here and always now,
Yet encompassing all that has ever been.

It is life lived to the full;
Every second contains a lifetime.
It is every loved one ever loved
And every loving face ever known.
It is abundant purpose,
Yet perfect repose.
Life is eternal;
Eternity is Life Itself.

I Saw You Today My Beloved

I saw you today my beloved,
You stood before my eyes
Like a beautiful presence of light.
Beautiful, graceful;
Full of smiling love.

I saw you today my beloved.
Rays of colour
Followed around you
Like the spray of water from a waterfall.
My heart is full, almost to bursting,
Since I saw you there, my beloved.

When you gently turned,
And returned,
I was not left without you.
I am never truly without you.
For you have left your presence inside me.
My heart still feels your beauty,
And sees your smile.

How can I ever be without you?
Since I saw you today, my beloved.

Let's Go Deeper, My Love

Let's go deeper, my love;
Deeper into this beautiful mystery,
The mystery that you call life,
And which I have found;
That which you call death.
Let's go deeper, my love.
You in your mystery,
And I in mine.
For in truth we are in the same mystery,
Discovering no end to its beauty
And its wondrous sights and experiences.

Let's go deeper, my love.
We could go back,
But there is no clear way back.
We can go forward,
Though we do not yet know the Way.
There is a strange certainty that
The way forward is certain.
While backwards steps have been trodden before,
We know what they bring.
Our souls long for that which is beyond.

Let's go deeper, my love.
Let us trust as we go.
Trusting in truth,
Trusting in love.
Trust for one another,
Trusting in our true selves.

Let's go deeper, my love
And meet from time to time
In the midst of inexpressible beauty,
And joy.
If we go ever deeper, my love,
One day, in some realm of joy,
We will be One.
And the journey will be done.

Nothing Ends

Nothing ends; I am still
As I always was and forever will be.
Part of God, yet still myself.
The one you loved,
And still love.

Nothing has ended; I am still here.
Forever One with you;
Part of you.
Find me in joy.
Do not seek for me in sorrow
Or you will think me as gone,
Far from you when sorrow
Casts its shadow across your heart.
Seek me in joy,
Find me in Light;
Laugh with me.
Do not think that tears will find me.
Come to me in love,
Dance with me in life.
Do not look for me in death,
For there is no death.

How can I be found where I am not?
Nothing ends; I still love,
Love you; and always will.
For love always is,
Always was and forever will be.
And so am I.
Nothing ends.

Vibration Is...

The word of God.
The basic sound in all creation.
Aum.
Amen.

Vibration creates all realised existence.
Without vibration all is pure spirit.
When spirit sends forth its vibration
Creation springs into being.
Vibration is in perfect harmony
With its Source.

It is the Breath of God.
The Word of God.
The Holy Spirit.
Energy, light and matter
Ride upon vibration's frequencies.

Vibration is not located anywhere;
Vibration is Everywhere.
Until vibration was sent forth
Everywhere did not exist.

What was before the Universe?
Vibration called the Universe into being.
Vibration is motion.
All that is,
All that ever can be,
Is dependent upon vibration.
Be still.
Do you not perceive it?
Do you not hear it?

The vibration that sustains
A million, million universes.
That creates a metaverse
As silent as No-thing.
As resonant as a trillion-piece orchestra.
Vibration is.
It simply is.

The Glimpse Behind The Veil

I asked to be granted to see beyond;
Behind the veil that is in itself beautiful,
But limiting.
Illusionary.

I asked to be able to see;
To see with eyes that behold what is not,
Rather than stare at what appears to be.

I asked to be granted vision;
Access to realms unspeakable
With words uttered with voice,
And heard with ears.

I asked to join with the wondrous realms,
And to behold a glimpse;
Just a glimpse,
Of the world where loved ones are;
Where life abounds
With colours and light and joy untold.

I asked,
And on this day, in this place,
It was granted...
And now speech falls silent
And bows to the wonder of it all.

Divine Mother

I will never forget,
Nor be the same again
Since seeing your beauty
Revealed to me behind the veil.

There is no colour on earth
To match your indescribable colour;
No light to stand beside yours.
The sun is dim;
The moon is dark;
The stars are old
Against your brilliance,
Your radiance,
Your now-ness,
Your all-ness.

I prostrate myself before you;
Before your beauty and wonder
And thank you,
That you should come to me
Today.

I am with you always.
I am the Father,
I am the Mother,
I am the Child.

The Secret Book of John 1:16

The Light That Shines from Heaven

There is a different order of Light
That shines from Heaven itself.
Just as a diamond shines brightly
In a world of lesser gems.
So the true Light is there,
Shining brightly in an order of Light
Too bright for our normal eyes to see.

It is in this Light that you live
And shine,
Always, forever, constantly.
It is a healing Light,
A nourishing Light,
A loving Light.
It shone on me today, my love.
We both shared this Light;
This love
For a short but precious time today.
Once more we both were One.
No longer, I here, and you elsewhere,
But both together on one plane.
That place radiated Light
More bright than any I have ever known.

Thank you... thank you.
A million, million thanks
For one small bathing
In that glorious brightness.
Until next time we meet again.
Our love undiminished.
You in Light,
And I in praise of that Light.
Thank you.

Justice Is...

Love.

Without Love, life would end
Without reward or payment.

O, without Love, suffering would have no purpose
And death would be the end.

But Justice is Love's reward
When all becomes Light;
Where suffering is repaid in full
And where death is the gift of unending joy.
Perfect Love is the certainty of perfect Justice.

When this perishable body puts on imperishability,
And this mortal body puts on immortality,
Then the saying that is written will be fulfilled:
"Death has been swallowed up in victory."

1 Corinthians 15:54

You Can See Me

I am still me;
Spirit am I.
A beautiful, swirling ball of light.
I can dance.
I am motion.
I am never still as you would think of still.
I can soar.
I can float.
I can fly.
I am energy and colour; luminous light.
I am intelligence.
I am thought.
I am mind.
I am all around you all the time,
Yet I am not here,
Nor there;
In my world,
I simply am.

You can see me when you are still,
Sometimes a luminous bird;
Often a shining butterfly.
Look closer.

I am an illuminated fairy.
An angel.
We sometimes dress up and appear as we were,
Your wife,
A mother,
A father,
A friend.
I am still these for I have been all those,
And will be again.
And so will you.
There is no day; no night when I am not there
All around you.
For there is no day,
Nor night,
Nor birth,
Nor death.
It but appears to you that it is while in your body,
But once free,
You too will soar,
And float,
And fly.
Farewell for now
Until you see me again in the silence,
In the wonder,
In the beauty,
Of the deep.

Beyond God

Behind thick clouds,
There shines the sun.

Behind closed eyelids,
Comes forth light.

Beyond fear,
Love emerges.

Beyond death,
Life is revealed.

Beyond life,
God is.

Beyond God,
Is God.

God's form is not in the field of vision:
no one sees God with mortal eye.
God is seen by a pure heart and by a mind that is pure.
Those that know God attain Life immortal.

Katha Upanishad 6

The World Of Spirit

It is clearly an incredible journey
Into the world of spirit;
A journey I have hardly begun.
A veil I long to travel through
And beyond.
For even the start of the journey
Is glorious;
More beautiful than all beauty there is on earth.
Colour beyond description;
Wonder and mystery beyond delight;
Peace and joy beyond mere pleasure.
This is a journey I long to take.
To reach a destination
Bathed in pure love.
Oh, that I may go some day,
To the end of an endless journey,
To a placeless destination
That reaches into eternity;
That touches the formless;
That knows the unknowable.
Dive deep into this journey
Leading to everywhere.
Re~unite with everyone.
Leave nothing by releasing everything,
And travel on and on
Through countless worlds and galaxies,
Until you arrive where you began.
Pure, blissful ecstasy;
Love uncreated;
Known and knowing,
All yet No~thing,
Love.

The World Is...

God's dream;
Consciousness realising itself.
Earth is God's body;
The world, God's clothing.
It is a beautiful dream
Peopled with beauty
And awesome phenomena.

The world is also a nightmare;
Full of suffering, change and loss.
Sickness and death appear
Along with hatred and greed.

The world is a happy dream
Bursting with laughter and life.
The world is sorrow;
A dream of sadness and tears.

The world is a dream
Out of which to awaken
And discover Life;
That which is changeless –
Reality.

Our world is the dream
Created by ourselves
To punish us for feeling so unworthy
Of Love,
Of Life.

Yet it can be a dream of Heaven on Earth;
A dream in which Love has come to heal
The nightmare;
To reveal the Truth
To offer Life
Gift-wrapped in Love –
God's World.

Never Be The Same Again

From now on you will never be the same.
You have discovered a level of reality
That has been veiled from your eyes until now.

There is no going back;
Only deeper.

Deeper into Christ Consciousness
Where so great a beauty exists
That mere earth light is as night
And earth night is as sleep to you.

Rise up and come with us into the Light.

The True Reality

There is an order of light;
A level of beauty;
A quality of peace;
A presence
That is beyond description.
It is Reality.
Once entered, a new world
Is presented.
Only slightly as yet,
For the wonder is so great
That the soul at first withdraws
While wanting, needing, desiring
To go further in.
In, in, into that divine Light.
Even the swirling outer glow
Is divine peace.
Yet the light of the Christ
Is of a different order
That makes the sun dim
And the moon seem a mere candle.
Rest a while in the light;
Allow it to bathe you
In its wondrous glow –
All else falls at its feet.
Earthly beauty bows to its glory.
The spark of light
That is the Christ,
That is your own true Self,
Once found, like a pearl of great price;
Is to be valued and treasured;
For it is Life itself.

True Peace And Joy

If only you knew
What it was to die
You would want to do it again and again.
It is like taking off a tight shoe,
Like shedding an old, unwanted garment
Too tight for your body;
A garment too restricting for the soul.

The tranquillity;
The silence filled with a sound
Too subtle for physical ears to hear.
The beauty;
The colour;
Too deep, too beautiful
For physical words to describe.
Not wanting to return
To a body in physical form,
Yet never leaving your own awareness of self.
Then on, on, onwards into the known Unknown.

No fear;
Never alone;
Able always to return
Yet never needing to.
This is dying;
This is true peace and joy.

Heaven Is...

Home.

Within and around you,
It is neither here nor there.
Not up or down.

Heaven is here and Heaven is now.

The Soul of all beings, living within the body,
Is eternal and cannot be harmed.
Therefore, do not grieve.

Bhagavad Gita 2:30

Death Is...

An illusion.

Nothing at all.

Afterword

I hope that you have found comfort and help from something that you have read in this book that has spoken directly to you from the Heart of Love. Maybe you know somebody who is hurting right now, especially from the loss of a most precious loved one; if so, please pass this book on to them or contact me for a copy so that you can give it to them in their time of need.

One thing that we all have in common as human beings in this wonderful, unending, often difficult journey in Life is the pain felt at the loss of our loved ones. None will escape; we all experience grief. In the same way as love for family and friends teaches us more about the Love of God, so grief teaches us more about our own dying process, and hopefully, helps us to prepare for our own transition. There is no death; we go on to another dimension of existence. This life is to be lived fully so that we are happy in our life on earth and happy in Life beyond our life on the earth.

As souls who are currently experiencing life in a physical body, you and I are limitless in our potential to create. The consciousness of Christ, which is the consciousness of our Real Self, is able to create and recreate worlds and universes. If you are recently bereaved, you may think and feel that all is lost; that you have not only lost your loved one but that you have lost your very self. Within you is the all-powerful Christ Consciousness, out of which you, your loved ones and the world around you has sprung. You can, and will, recreate yourself. You will never lose your love for – or your memories – of those you have loved in this world; nor need you ever... but if you follow the Spirit you will discover that you will evolve into somebody who is amazing – someone you never thought you could become...

For further copies of 'Silent Voices from Forever',
email info@happydream.co.uk or visit www.happydream.co.uk